# William Shakespeare

# The Merchant of Venice

First published 2015 by Walker Books Ltd
87 Vauxhall Walk, London SE11 5HJ

2 4 6 8 10 9 7 5 3 1

This book has been typeset in Kennerly Regular

Printed and bound in China

British Library Cataloguing in Publication Data:
a catalogue record for this book is available from the British Library

ISBN 978-14063-6275-6

www.walker.co.uk

For Oscar

# William Shakespeare
# The Merchant of Venice

### Retold by
## Marcia Williams

WALKER
BOOKS

# Contents

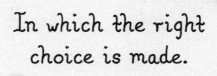

In which the right
choice is made.

Long ago in Venice, there lived a merchant
named Antonio. He was honest and
generous and well loved by his friends.
When Antonio's luck was in, and his ships
arrived safely at port with their rich cargo,
he would lend his money to whoever asked
and expect no interest.

Antonio was particularly generous to
his good friend Bassanio. Bassanio was a

young man of noble birth, but he was very poor and had often borrowed from Antonio. Now Bassanio had decided that the time had come to clear his debts once and for all.

"To you, Antonio, I owe the most, in money and in love," he declared.

"My purse, my person, my extremest means, lie all unlock'd to your occasions," promised the good-hearted merchant.

"In Belmont is a lady richly left," said Bassanio. "And she is fair, and fairer than that word."

Gradually it unfolded that Bassanio was in love with Portia, a rich heiress who lived in Belmont, near Venice. Bassanio thought his love might be returned, and if it was, he would never have to borrow money again. The problem was that to travel to Portia's estate and to court her in a fitting manner, Bassanio needed three thousand ducats!

"Thou know'st that all my fortunes are at sea. Neither have I money nor commodity to raise a present sum," said Antonio. But he decided to see if he could borrow money against his good name until his ships arrived.

Antonio and Bassanio went to the Rialto, where the money lenders gathered. They asked Shylock, a Jew, to lend them the money and were surprised when he agreed – it was well known that Shylock hated Antonio. He hated him because Antonio stole his customers by lending money without interest, and also because Antonio treated him with scorn. Antonio willingly admitted this – but Bassanio needed money. For him, Antonio was willing to overlook his dislike of Shylock.

"Well, Shylock, shall we be beholding to you?" asked Antonio with no great warmth.

"You call me misbeliever, cut-throat dog, and spit upon my Jewish gaberdine," said Shylock. "Well then, it now appears you need my help."

"If thou wilt lend this money, lend it not as to thy friends, but lend it rather to thine enemy," said Antonio.

Strangely, Shylock agreed to lend the money to Antonio without interest. Shylock

suggested another bond: if the money was not returned in three months, as Antonio promised it would be, he must pay with a pound of his flesh. "An equal pound, to be cut off and taken in what part of your body pleaseth me," said Shylock.

This was just by way of a jest, Shylock said, but it didn't seem so to Bassanio. "You shall not seal to such a bond for me!" he cried, horrified.

"Why, fear not, man," Antonio reassured

him. "I will not forfeit it. Within these two months, I do expect return of thrice three times the value of this bond."

So Antonio rashly agreed. He went with Shylock to the notary and signed the bond.

With the money in his purse, Bassanio prepared for his visit to Portia. He acquired a small retinue of servants and bought himself some richly embroidered

garments, befitting a young man about to woo his love.

His friend Gratiano begged to accompany him. "You must not deny me," Gratiano said. Bassanio laughingly agreed, but he warned his friend not to be too wild or loud in case it set Portia against his suit. For many fine nobles had tried to win the lady for their wife, but none had succeeded. This was partly because Portia did not like any of them, and partly because of her father.

Before he had died, Portia's father had made three caskets with a riddle inscribed on each one. One casket was made of gold, and read: "Who chooseth me shall gain what many men desire." Another was

made of silver, and read: "Who chooseth
me shall get as much as he deserves."
The last one was made of lead, and read:
"Who chooseth me must give and hazard

all he hath." Portia's father had decreed
that the first suitor to pick the casket that
contained a portrait of his daughter would
win her hand.

"By my troth, Nerissa, my little body is aweary of this great world," sighed Portia to her maid, after yet another suitor had tried and failed to choose the correct casket.

At first, the arrival of another suitor did not excite Portia, but when she heard it was Bassanio her mood changed. Bassanio had been at Belmont for just a few days when it became obvious to all that he and Portia loved each other.

Bassanio was eager to know his fate and try his hand at choosing the casket, but Portia had seen many other suitors fail. "I pray you, tarry: pause a day or two before you hazard," she begged. "For in choosing wrong I lose your company."

"Let me choose; for as I am I live upon the rack," said Bassanio, who already found it impossible to imagine his future without Portia.

"Away then! I am lock'd in one of them. If you do love me, you will find me out," said Portia, sounding more certain than she felt.

So the caskets were brought and laid before Bassanio. Portia, Nerissa and Gratiano watched him nervously. Gold, silver, or lead? Which should Bassanio choose?

He stared at the caskets long and hard. "So may the outward shows be least themselves: the world is still deceived with ornament," Bassanio said to himself.

"Therefore, thou gaudy gold, I will none of thee. Nor none of thee," he said, looking at the silver casket. "But thou, thou meagre lead, here choose I: joy be the consequence!"

With a shaking hand, he turned the key in the lead casket … and found his true love's portrait! Everyone clapped their hands in delight. Portia and Bassanio

hugged each other with relief. When
Bassanio confessed that he had many
debts and no wealth of his own, Portia
put his mind at rest, promising that she
had wealth enough for both of them.

"This house, these servants, and this
same myself are yours, my lord. I give them
with this ring; which when you part from,
lose, or give away, let it presage the ruin of

your love," said Portia, handing Bassanio a
ring.

Bassanio took it gratefully and swore
he would never part with it. Then, to
everyone's surprise and delight, Nerissa and
Gratiano announced that they too had fallen

in love. So Nerissa gave Gratiano a ring
and, just as Bassanio had done, Gratiano
promised never to part with this token of
Nerissa's love.

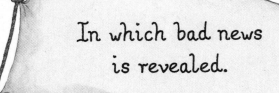

In which bad news
is revealed.

Amid all the joy, Bassanio's friend Lorenzo
arrived. He and Shylock's daughter Jessica
had been courting, but Shylock had

forbidden their marriage and had threatened
to disinherit Jessica. Their love was stronger
than Shylock's threats, so they had eloped to
Belmont. But they brought grave news from
Venice: Antonio's ships had not docked,
and the three months that Shylock had
allowed for the loan were up. Shylock was
demanding his bond – the pound of flesh.
Antonio's life was in danger.

"What sum owes he the Jew?" asked
Portia.

"For me, three thousand ducats," said Bassanio in great distress.

"What, no more? You shall have gold to pay the petty debt twenty times over," said Portia, trying to comfort Bassanio.

So that Bassanio would have easy access to Portia's money, the couples decided to marry immediately. Then Bassanio and Gratiano left for Venice to try to save Antonio.

"Since I have your good leave to go away,

I will make haste; but, till I come again, no
bed shall be guilty of my stay," promised
Bassanio, kissing his new wife.

Left behind, Portia wondered how she
could help Bassanio's friend, for she hated
to see her husband in distress. She decided
to write to her cousin, the learned lawyer
Doctor Bellario. She asked him to send
lawyers' clothes and books about the law
to Venice. Then Portia asked Lorenzo and
Jessica to look after her house, and said

she and Nerissa would move into the local monastery until their husbands returned.

"Come on, Nerissa: I have work in hand that you yet know not of. We'll see our husbands before they think of us," said Portia, trying to hurry her maid.

"Shall they see us?" asked Nerissa.

"They shall, Nerissa," smiled her mistress, with a twinkle in her eye.

In which a court
case is heard.

A few days later, Shylock brought his case
against Antonio to the duke's court in
Venice. Bassanio was there with Portia's
money, but because the three months had
expired, Shylock refused to take the larger
sum Bassanio offered. He wanted revenge
on his old enemy and was insisting on his
pound of Antonio's flesh.

"How shalt thou hope for mercy,

rendering none?" asked the duke.

"What judgement shall I dread, doing
no wrong?" replied Shylock. "The pound
of flesh, which I demand of him, is dearly
bought; 'tis mine and I will have it."

The whole court was horrified, but
Shylock would not relent. "He hath
disgraced me, laughed at my losses, mocked
at my gains: and what's his reason? I am
a Jew. Hath not a Jew eyes? Hath not a

Jew hands, organs, dimensions, senses, affections, passions? If you prick us, do we not bleed? If you tickle us, do we not laugh? If you poison us, do we not die? And if you wrong us, shall we not revenge?"

So the duke sent for an expert, Doctor Bellario, for advice. The lawyer was unwell but sent in his place a promising pupil and his clerk. Those present at court felt little confidence in this youth, for he looked too

 young to wield much wisdom. The young lawyer soon confirmed their views by announcing that the law stood against Antonio. Shylock was delighted and began to sharpen his knife.

"Why dost thou whet thy knife so earnestly?" cried out Bassanio.

"To cut the forfeiture from that bankrupt there," said Shylock.

 The lawyer then asked Shylock to be merciful and

to drop the charge. "The quality of mercy
is not strain'd, it droppeth as the gentle
rain from heaven upon the place beneath,"
explained the lawyer. "It is twice bless'd;
it blesseth him that gives and him that
takes."

Yet it seemed
that Shylock was
without mercy. "I
crave the law," he
cried.

"I am arm'd and well prepar'd," said
Antonio, thinking he was about to die.

The lawyer
stopped Shylock's
eager hand. He
warned Shylock

that the bond allowed him to take a pound
of flesh exactly. "Shed thou no blood, nor
cut thou less, nor more, but just a pound of
flesh," warned the lawyer, calling for scales
to be brought.

If Shylock
spilled one drop of
blood, or cut one
hair's weight over

the pound, he would break the law. Then he risked death or the loss of his estate. It seemed this lawyer had more wisdom than the court had thought. Shylock dropped his knife. He decided that he would take the money after all. "Let the Christian go," he muttered.

"Tarry, Jew. The law hath yet another hold on you," said the lawyer, explaining

that as Shylock had sought to kill a citizen of
Venice, the punishment was death, should
the duke decree it.

"That thou shalt see the difference of our
spirits, I pardon thee thy life before thou ask
it," announced the duke.

The duke went on to tell Shylock that
half his wealth must go to Antonio and
the other half to the state. But Antonio
didn't want Shylock's money. Instead he
asked that his half of Shylock's estate
should be given to Shylock's daughter,

Jessica. So it was agreed, and Shylock left the court humiliated and muttering oaths against all the world.

The lawyer had saved Antonio's life! Bassanio was overwhelmed with relief. He tried to give the lawyer the three thousand ducats that Antonio had owed Shylock, but the lawyer would not take a fee. Instead he asked for Bassanio's ring. Bassanio refused, for it was the ring that Portia had given him.

"My lord Bassanio, let him have the ring,"

begged Antonio, for to him a ring seemed a
paltry reward for the lawyer who had saved
his life.

"Go, Gratiano; run and overtake him; give
him the ring," sighed Bassanio, taking it off
his finger.

Gratiano went after the lawyer with the
ring, which he gratefully accepted. The
lawyer's clerk then persuaded Gratiano
to part with his ring too. Both he and

Bassanio looked down at their naked
fingers and wondered what they would
tell their wives.

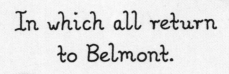

In which all return
to Belmont.

Bassanio, Gratiano and Antonio did not

tarry in Venice, but returned to Belmont as

quickly as the journey allowed. When they reached Portia's home, they never guessed that Portia and Nerissa had only returned a few moments before them.

"You are welcome home, my lord," cried Portia.

"Give welcome to my friend: this is the man, this is Antonio," said Bassiano.

At first the wives seemed pleased to see their husbands. Then Nerissa looked at

Gratiano's hands and asked where the ring was that she had given him. "You swore to me, when I did give it you, that you would wear it till your hour of death!" she shouted.

"A quarrel, ho, already! What's the matter?" asked Portia.

Soon both Gratiano and Bassanio were in trouble over their lost rings!

"Sweet Portia, if you did know to whom I gave the ring," pleaded Bassanio.

Both wives were unrelenting and claimed to be deeply upset and offended.

"I am the unhappy subject of these quarrels," said Antonio. He begged the wives to forgive their husbands.

Finally, Portia relented. She bade Antonio

pass Bassanio a ring. "And bid him keep it better than the other," she said.

"By heaven! It is the same I gave the doctor!" cried Bassanio.

Then Nerissa relented as well and gave Gratiano a ring. This ring also seemed very familiar. The two men stared at the rings and then at each other. Surely these

were the very rings that they had given
away?

"Were you the doctor and I knew you
not?" asked Bassanio, turning to his wife in
amazement.

"Were you the clerk?" asked Gratiano,
looking at Nerissa in disbelief.

It was true. Portia had been the young

lawyer who had saved Antonio's life, and
Nerissa her clerk! The two men could not
believe how blind they had been.

There was more good news to come:
Nerissa told Jessica that even though
she had eloped with Lorenzo, she would
inherit Shylock's wealth. And Antonio
discovered that his ships had finally come

safely into harbour. At last the friends
could celebrate and laugh at the husbands
who had not known their own wives!

"Well," chuckled Gratiano, swinging

his wife high into the air, "while I live, I'll fear no other thing so sore as keeping safe Nerissa's ring."

**WILLIAM SHAKESPEARE** was a popular playwright, poet and actor who lived in Elizabethan England. He married in Stratford-upon-Avon aged eighteen and had three children, although one died in childhood. Shakespeare then moved to London, where he wrote 39 plays and over 150 sonnets, many of which are still very popular today. In fact, his plays are performed more often than those of any other playwright, and he died 450 years ago! His gravestone includes a curse against interfering with his burial place, possibly to

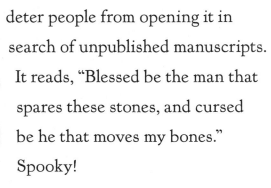

deter people from opening it in search of unpublished manuscripts. It reads, "Blessed be the man that spares these stones, and cursed be he that moves my bones." Spooky!

**MARCIA WILLIAMS'** mother was a novelist and her father a playwright, so it's not surprising that Marcia ended up an author herself. Although she never trained formally as an artist, she found that motherhood, and the time she spent later as a nursery school teacher, inspired her to start writing and illustrating children's books.

Marcia's books bring to life some of the world's all-time favourite stories and some colourful historical characters. Her hilarious retellings and clever observations will have children laughing out loud and coming back for more!

# More retellings from Marcia Williams

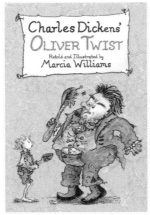

ISBN 978-1-4063-5692-2

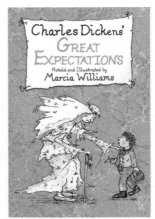

ISBN 978-1-4063-5693-9

ISBN 978-1-4063-5694-6

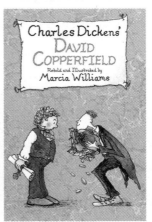

ISBN 978-1-4063-5695-3

Available from all good booksellers

www.walker.co.uk